Goldilocks
and the BIG Mess
the

CW00921234

Written by Smriti Prasadam-Halls
Illustrated by Andy Rowland

For Tom – S.P-H.

One day Goldilocks was walking in the woods. She came to a small house. She looked inside but no one was at home.

She saw three bowls of porridge
sitting on the table.
"I'll be helpful and eat some porridge!"
said Goldilocks, picking up a spoon.

"Ouch!" The first bowl was too hot.

"Yuck!" The second bowl was too cold.

The third bowl of porridge was perfect so Goldilocks gobbled it up.

She was just leaving when she fell over
a cushion.

"I'd better put *this* on a chair,"
said Goldilocks. "Where does it go?"

Crash!

The first and second chairs were
much too big.
The third chair was perfect
but when Goldilocks sat on it ...
Crash!

As she tidied up, Goldilocks spotted a blanket.

"I'd better put *that* away," she said.

When she got upstairs,
Goldilocks needed a rest.
It was very, *very*
hard work being helpful.

The first bed was too hard to lie on and the second bed was too soft. The third bed was perfect and Goldilocks soon fell fast asleep.

The house belonged to a family
of bears. They were very surprised
when they came home.
"Who's been eating our porridge?"
they gasped.

They ran into the living room.
"Who's been sitting in
our chairs?" they growled.

They stomped into the bedroom.
"Who's been sleeping in our beds?"
they howled.

"Look!" squeaked Baby Bear.
"There's someone here!"

"Hello," said Goldilocks. "I'm Goldilocks."
"What have you been doing in our
house?" asked Papa Bear.
"Helping, of course!" replied Goldilocks.

14

"*Helping?*" laughed the bears.

"Never mind," said Mama Bear.
"What about some tea?"
"Yes please!" said Goldilocks. "Shall I help?"
"**NO!**" shouted everyone.